This Book Belongs To:

_____

COPYRIGHT © 2004 Nanci Bell
Gander Publishing
450 Front Street
Avila Beach, CA 93424
805-541-5523 • 800-554-1819

VISUALIZING AND VERBALIZING AND V/V ARE
REGISTERED TRADEMARKS OF NANCI BELL.

14   13   12   11   5   6   7   8

ISBN 0-945856-38-5   978-0-945856-38-2

Overview and Directions

This workbook is offered to provide a wider selection of material for practice developing gestalt imagery and language comprehension with the *Visualizing and Verbalizing for Language Comprehension and Thinking*® (V/V®) program.

Following the steps of V/V®, detail and gestalt imagery are developed with Sentence by Sentence, Multiple Sentence, Whole Paragraph, and Paragraph by Paragraph V/V® stimulation.

The V/V® workbooks contain high-imagery stories and the following workbook activities:

- Imagery questions
- Picture summary exercises
- Word summary prompts
- Page summary prompts
- Main idea exercises
- Higher order thinking (HOT) questions
- Paragraph writing prompts

Before the student begins each story, he/she should decode each vocabulary word and visualize the meaning. This will help create imagery and develop contextual fluency. When answering imagery questions, the student may write phrases or partial sentences to describe his/her imagery.

These workbooks have been written specifically to help students learn and discover the wonder of the written word by improving gestalt imagery, critical thinking, and writing skills. Once these skills are developed, the possibilities are endless.

Remember, you can help students do this. You can do anything!

Nanci Bell
2004

There are three workbooks at each reading level:

Book A • Sentence by Sentence
Book B • Sentence by Sentence and Multiple Sentence
Book C • Multiple Sentence, Whole Paragraph, and Paragraph by Paragraph

---

Meet Ivan!

I am Ivan, King of the Neighborhood. I'm big and wide and full of pride!

I **love** to eat!

I **love** to sleep!

I am a cat!

1 Pirates Ahoy!

The pirates sailed through the open seas heading for their secret hideaway. With their large ship filled with gold and treasure, they wanted for a safe place to bury their loot. Suddenly a huge storm blew in. Strong winds and high waves pounded the ship. The ship and all its treasure sank to the bottom of the sea.

Vocabulary:

pirate: sailors who attack and rob ships
ahoy: a word used to get someone's attention, usually sailors
hideaway: a secret place
treasure: money and jewels
loot: stolen things

---

1 **First Sentence:** The pirates sailed through the open seas heading for their secret hideaway.

What did those words make you picture?_____
_____
_____

1. What did you picture for pirates?_____
_____

2. What did the sailing ship look like?_____
_____

3. What did you picture for the open sea?_____
_____

4. What did you picture for a "secret hideaway"?_____
_____

---

2 **Second Sentence:** With their large ship filled with gold and treasure, they wanted for a safe place to bury their loot.

What did those words make you picture?_____
_____
_____

1. What did you picture for their ship?_____
_____

2. What did you picture for the gold?_____
_____

3. What did you picture for the treasure?_____
_____

4. What did you picture for them wanting to bury their gold and treasure?
_____

3 **Third Sentence:** Suddenly a huge storm blew in.

What did those words make you picture?_____

_____

_____

1. What did you picture for the storm?_____

_____

2. What did you picture for the sky during the storm?_____

_____

3. What did you see the storm doing to their sailing ship?_____

_____

4. Were you picturing all this up close or from far away?_____

_____

4 **Fourth Sentence:** Strong winds and high waves pounded the ship.

What did those words make you picture?_____

_____

_____

1. What did you picture for the strong winds?_____

_____

2. What did you picture for the high waves?_____

_____

3. What did you see for the ship being pounded?_____

_____

4. What did you see the pirates doing during the storm?_____

_____

5 **Fifth Sentence:** The ship and all its treasure sank to the bottom of the sea.

What did those words make you picture?_____

_____

_____

1. What did you picture for the ship starting to sink?_____

_____

2. What did you see the pirates doing as the ship sank?_____

_____

3. What did you picture for the bottom of the sea?_____

_____

Picture Summary:

Number your images in order.

	The pirates wanted for a safe place to bury their loot.
	The ship and all its treasure sank to the bottom of the sea.
	The pirates sailed for their secret hideaway.
	Suddenly, a storm blew in and high waves pounded the ship.

Write a Word Summary:

_____

_____

_____

_____

Main Idea:

Check the box that best describes all your images—the main idea.

☐ A huge storm sank the pirate ship and all of its treasure as it was sailing to its hideaway.

☐ The pirates sailed through the sea on a ship filled with gold and treasure.

☐ A huge storm with strong winds and high waves pounded the pirate ship.

HOT Questions:

1. Why do you think the pirates were going to a secret hideaway?_____

_____

2. How do you think the pirates got the treasure?_____

_____

3. Why do you think the pirates wanted to bury their treasure?_____

_____

4. What do you think the pirates did when the ship started to sink?_____

_____

5. Do you think they had a way to survive? Explain. _____

_____

6. Why do you think the ship sank to the bottom of the sea?_____

_____

Make up a story about being a pirate.

_____

_____

_____

_____

_____

_____

_____

_____

_____

_____

_____

_____

_____

_____

_____

_____

Did you use all of the Structure Words? Check each one you used.

- ☐ What
- ☐ Size
- ☐ Color
- ☐ Number
- ☐ Shape
- ☐ Where
- ☐ Movement
- ☐ Mood
- ☐ Background
- ☐ Perspective
- ☐ When
- ☐ Sound

2 Smoke Jumper

A smoke jumper is a special fire fighter who puts out big forest fires. He flies in an airplane over burning forests. Then he straps on his parachute and jumps into the smoke-filled sky. The parachute floats him to the ground near the huge flames. Then he grabs his shovel and ax, and begins to fight the fire.

Vocabulary:

parachute: an umbrella-like sheet that lets a person float to the ground slowly
float: move slowly in the air

1 **First Sentence:** A smoke jumper is a special fire fighter who puts out big forest fires.

What did those words make you picture? _____

_____

1. What did you picture for the smoke jumper? _____

_____

2. Where did you see this happening? _____

_____

3. What did you picture for a forest fire? _____

_____

4. What did you see smoke jumpers doing to the forest fires? _____

2 **Second Sentence:** He flies in an airplane over burning forests.

What did those words make you picture? _____

_____

1. What did you picture the smoke jumper doing now? _____

_____

2. What did you picture for the plane? _____

_____

3. Where did you picture him flying? _____

_____

4. What did you picture for the burning forests? _____

3 **Third Sentence:** Then he straps on his parachute and jumps into the smoke-filled sky.

What did those words make you picture?_____

_____

_____

1. What did you picture the smoke jumper putting on?_____

_____

2. What did you picture for the parachute?_____

_____

3. What did you picture for him jumping into the sky?_____

_____

4. What did you picture for the sky?_____

_____

4 **Fourth Sentence:** The parachute floats him to the ground near the huge flames.

What did those words make you picture?_____

_____

_____

1. What did you picture for him floating to the ground?_____

_____

2. What did you see for the parachute as he floated down?_____

_____

3. What did you see for him landing on the ground?_____

_____

4. What did you picture for the huge flames?_____

_____

5 **Fifth Sentence:** Then he grabs his shovel and ax, and begins to fight the fire.

What did those words make you picture?_____

_____

_____

1. What did you picture for the smoke jumper fighting the fire?_____

_____

2. What did you picture for his ax?_____

_____

3. What did you picture him doing with the shovel?_____

_____

Picture Summary:

Number your images in order.

☐ The smoke jumper grabs his shovel and ax.

☐ The smoke jumper rides in an airplane over the fire.

☐ The smoke jumper begins to fight the fire.

☐ The smoke jumper parachutes out of the plane and floats down to the fire.

9

Critical Thinking

Write a Word Summary:

_____

_____

_____

_____

Main Idea:

Check the box that best describes all your images—the main idea.

☐ Smoke jumpers are fire fighters who parachute to big forest fires and fight the fire.

☐ The smoke jumper flies in an airplane over burning forests.

☐ The smoke jumper grabs his shovel and ax and begins to fight the fire.

HOT Questions:

1. Why do you think smoke jumpers use an airplane to go to the fires?_____

_____

2. Why do you think a smoke jumper might fly over the forest fire?_____

_____

3. Why do you think he parachutes down to the fire and doesn't just land the airplane?_____

_____

4. Why do you think he needs a shovel and an ax to fight the fire?_____

_____

5. Why do you think these fire fighters are called smoke jumpers?_____

_____

6. Do you think a smoke jumper is brave? Explain._____

_____

Make up a story about fighting a forest fire.

_____

_____

_____

_____

_____

_____

_____

_____

_____

_____

_____

_____

_____

_____

_____

_____

_____

_____

_____

_____

_____

Did you use all of the Structure Words? Check each one you used.

☐ What   ☐ Size   ☐ Color   ☐ Number   ☐ Shape   ☐ Where
☐ Movement   ☐ Mood   ☐ Background   ☐ Perspective   ☐ When   ☐ Sound

3 The Walking Stick

The long brown walking stick inches her way along a tree branch. With her thin stiff body and legs, the insect can only move very slowly. When a bird flies overhead, the insect stops. She does not move as the bird circles the branch, and then finally flies away. Only when the bird is gone will the walking stick move again.

Vocabulary:

walking stick: a long insect that looks like a stick
inches: moves very slowly
stiff: hard; not easy to move

---

1 **First Sentence:** The long brown walking stick inches her way along a tree branch.

What did those words make you picture?_____

_____

_____

1. What did you picture for the walking stick?_____

   _____

2. What color did you picture the walking stick?_____

   _____

3. What did you see for the walking stick "inching" along?_____

   _____

4. Where did you picture this happening—in a forest, a park, or...?_____

   _____

---

2 **Second Sentence:** With her thin stiff body and legs, the insect can only move very slowly.

What did those words make you picture?_____

_____

_____

1. What did you picture for the walking stick's body?_____

   _____

2. What did you picture for her legs?_____

   _____

3. How fast did you see the walking stick moving her legs?_____

   _____

4. Were you picturing this up close or from far away?_____

   _____

3 Third Sentence: When a bird flies overhead, the insect stops.

What did those words make you picture?_____

_____

_____

1. What did you picture for the bird?_____

_____

2. What color and size was the bird you pictured?_____

_____

3. What did you picture for the bird flying?_____

_____

4. What did you see the walking stick doing when the bird flew overhead?

_____

4 Fourth Sentence: She does not move as the bird circles the branch, and then finally flies away.

What did those words make you picture?_____

_____

_____

1. What did you see the walking stick doing when the bird flew above the branch?

_____

2. Where did you picture the walking stick?_____

_____

3. What did you picture for the bird circling?_____

_____

4. What did you see the bird doing after it circled the branch?_____

_____

5 Fifth Sentence: Only when the bird is gone will the walking stick move again.

What did those words make you picture?_____

_____

_____

1. Where did you picture the bird now?_____

_____

2. What did you see the walking stick doing after the bird flew away?

_____

3. What did it look like when she moved again?_____

_____

Picture Summary:

Number your images in order.

☐ The walking stick moves only after the bird is gone.

☐ The walking stick moves very slowly along a tree branch.

☐ The walking stick stops and stays very still.

☐ A bird circles the branch, but the walking stick doesn't move.

Critical Thinking

Write a Word Summary:

_____

_____

_____

_____

_____

Main Idea:

Check the box that best describes all your images—the main idea.

[ ] The long thin walking stick can easily hide from hungry birds.

[ ] The walking stick can only move very slowly.

[ ] The walking stick stops when a bird flies overhead.

HOT Questions:

1. Why do you think the insect is called a walking stick?_____

_____

2. Why do you think the walking stick can only move very slowly?_____

_____

3. What do you think the bird was looking for?_____

_____

4. Why do you think the insect stopped moving when the bird flew overhead?_____

_____

5. Why do you think the bird flew away?_____

_____

6. Do you think many walking sticks get eaten by birds? Why or why not?_____

_____

Make up a story about Willie the Walking Stick out for a stroll until he falls off a branch.

_____

_____

_____

_____

_____

_____

_____

_____

_____

_____

_____

_____

_____

_____

_____

_____

_____

Did you use all of the Structure Words? Check each one you used.

☐ What   ☐ Size   ☐ Color   ☐ Number   ☐ Shape   ☐ Where
☐ Movement   ☐ Mood   ☐ Background   ☐ Perspective   ☐ When   ☐ Sound

4 Archer Fish

The black and white archer fish looked up at the trees that hung over the river. He was searching for insects on the low branches. Then, he spotted a fly and swam under the branch, moving his mouth just out of the water. With careful aim, he spit a long stream of water at the insect. The water knocked the fly into the water and the fish ate his lunch.

Vocabulary:

archer: someone who uses a bow and arrow
aim: to carefully point at something
stream: a long flow of water

---

1 **First Sentence:** The black and white archer fish looked up at the trees that hung over the river.

What did those words make you picture?_____

_____

_____

1. What color and size did you picture the archer fish?_____

2. What did you see for the fish looking at the trees?_____

3. What did you picture for the river?_____

4. What did you see for the branches hanging over the water?_____

---

2 **Second Sentence:** He was searching for insects on the low branches.

What did those words make you picture?_____

_____

_____

1. What did you picture for the archer fish searching?_____

2. Did you see him swimming back and forth or was he still?_____

3. What did you picture for the insects?_____

4. What did you see for the insects on the branches?_____

3 **Third Sentence:** Then, he spotted a fly and swam under the branch, moving his mouth just out of the water.

What did those words make you picture?_____

_____

_____

1. What did you picture for the fish as he spotted the fly?_____

_____

2. What did you picture for the fly?_____

_____

3. What did you see for the fish swimming under the branch?_____

_____

4. What did you picture for the fish moving his mouth?_____

_____

4 **Fourth Sentence:** With careful aim, he spit a long stream of water at the insect.

What did those words make you picture?_____

_____

_____

1. What did you picture for the fish taking aim?_____

_____

2. What did you see for the fish spitting?_____

_____

3. What did you see for the stream of water he spit?_____

_____

4. What did you see for the fly now?_____

_____

5 **Fifth Sentence:** The water knocked the fly into the water and the fish ate his lunch.

What did those words make you picture?_____

_____

_____

1. What did you see the stream of water doing to the fly?_____

_____

2. Where did you picture the fly falling?_____

_____

3. How did you see the fish eating his lunch?_____

_____

Picture Summary:

Number your images in order.

☐ The water knocked the fly into the water and the fish ate his lunch.

☐ The fish swam under the branch and moved his mouth out of the water.

☐ The archer fish looked up at the trees that hung over the river to find an insect.

☐ The fish spit a stream of water at the insect.

Write a Word Summary:

—————————————————————————————————

—————————————————————————————————

—————————————————————————————————

—————————————————————————————————

Main Idea:

Check the box that best describes all your images—the main idea.

☐ The archer fish searches for insects on the branches.

☐ The archer fish moves its mouth just out of the water so he can catch a fly and eat it.

☐ The archer fish can spit streams of water to knock insects off low branches that hang over the water.

HOT Questions:

1. Why do you think the archer fish was searching the branches?_____

_____

2. Why do you think he moved just below a branch?_____

_____

3. Why do you think the fish moved his mouth out of the water?_____

_____

4. Why do you think the archer fish needed to aim carefully?_____

_____

5. Where do you think he got the water to spit at the fly?_____

_____

6. Why do you think this fish is called an "archer fish"?_____

_____

Make up a story about a fishing trip and a storm.

_____

_____

_____

_____

_____

_____

_____

_____

_____

_____

_____

_____

_____

_____

_____

_____

_____

_____

Did you use all of the Structure Words? Check each one you used.

☐ What   ☐ Size   ☐ Color   ☐ Number   ☐ Shape   ☐ Where
☐ Movement   ☐ Mood   ☐ Background   ☐ Perspective   ☐ When   ☐ Sound

5 Snow Monkeys

As the weather begins to grow cold, the snow monkeys of Japan head to the hot springs. In the winter, their thick gray fur keeps them warm. But on the very coldest days, they like to sit in the hot water of the springs. With their bright red faces peering through the steam, the monkeys sit quietly away from the cold weather.

Vocabulary:

snow monkeys: monkeys that live in Japan and are about 3 feet long
Japan: an island nation in Asia
hot springs: natural pools of hot water that come out of the ground
peering: looking
steam: hot water vapor in the air

---

1 **First Sentence:** As the weather begins to grow cold, the snow monkeys of Japan head to the hot springs.

What did those words make you picture?_____

_____

1. What did you picture for the snow monkeys?_____

   _____

2. What did you see for the weather growing cold?_____

   _____

3. What did you picture for the hot springs?_____

   _____

4. Were you picturing this from close up or far away?_____

---

2 **Second Sentence:** In the winter, their thick gray fur keeps them warm.

What did those words make you picture?_____

_____

1. What did you picture for winter weather?_____

   _____

2. What did you picture for the monkeys' fur?_____

   _____

3. What color did you picture the monkeys' fur?_____

   _____

4. What did you see for the monkeys being warm?_____

3 **Third Sentence:** But on the very coldest days, they like to sit in the hot water of the springs.

What did those words make you picture?_____

_____

_____

1. What did you picture for very cold days?_____

_____

2. What did you see for the monkeys in the hot water?_____

_____

3. Did you picture the monkeys sitting or standing in the hot springs?___

_____

4. What did you picture to show that the water is hot?_____

4 **Fourth Sentence:** With their bright red faces peering through the steam, the monkeys sit quietly away from the cold weather.

What did those words make you picture?_____

_____

_____

1. What did you picture for the steam coming off the hot springs?_____

_____

2. What did you picture for the faces of the monkeys?_____

_____

3. What did you see for the monkeys' faces peering through the steam?

_____

4. What did you see the monkey doing while in the hot springs?_____

_____

Picture Summary:

Number your images in order.

▢ The snow monkeys of Japan go to the hot springs when it gets cold.

▢ They like to sit in the hot springs on the coldest days.

▢ Their fur normally keeps them warm in winter.

▢ Their red faces peer out of the steam as they sit in the hot water.

Write a Word Summary:

_____

_____

_____

_____

_____

_____

Critical Thinking

Main Idea:

Check the box that best describes all your images—the main idea.

☐ The snow monkeys sit in the hot water of the springs in Japan.

☐ The snow monkeys' red faces peer through the steam of the hot springs in Japan.

☐ When the weather gets cold, the snow monkeys of Japan sit in the hot springs to stay warm.

HOT Questions:

1. Why do you think the monkeys are called "snow monkeys"?_____

_____

2. Why do you think the monkeys need to have thick fur?_____

_____

3. Why do you think the monkeys go to the hot springs?_____

_____

4. Why do you think the monkeys sit quietly in the water?_____

_____

5. Why do you think they peer through the steam?_____

_____

6. Do you think the monkeys visit the hot springs in the summer? Why or why not?_____

_____

7. What do you think might happen if there were no hot springs?_____

_____

Make up a story about Sally the Snow Monkey going to the hot springs to play.

_____

_____

_____

_____

_____

_____

_____

_____

_____

_____

_____

_____

_____

_____

_____

_____

_____

Did you use all of the Structure Words? Check each one you used.

☐ What   ☐ Size   ☐ Color   ☐ Number   ☐ Shape   ☐ Where
☐ Movement ☐ Mood   ☐ Background   ☐ Perspective ☐ When   ☐ Sound

6 Michelangelo

Michelangelo often went to the quarry to look at the raw blocks of marble. He went to an enormous one and pressed his cheek against the cool white stone. His fingers ran over the smooth surface. Finally, he began to imagine a figure he thought was inside. The great sculptor picked up his chisel and began to sculpt the statue of David.

Vocabulary:

Michelangelo: an Italian sculptor, architect, and artist
quarry: a place where stone is dug out of the ground
marble: a hard rock that can be white or colored
chisel: a flat tool with a sharp cutting edge used to chip away pieces of stone

---

1 First Sentence: Michelangelo often went to the quarry to look at the raw blocks of marble.

What did those words make you picture?_____

_____

1. What did you picture for Michelangelo?_____

   _____

2. What did you picture for the quarry?_____

   _____

3. What color did you picture for the blocks of marble?_____

   _____

4. What did you see for Michelangelo looking at the marble?_____

---

2 Second Sentence: He went to an enormous one and pressed his cheek against the cool white stone.

What did those words make you picture?_____

_____

1. What did you picture for the enormous block of marble?_____

   _____

2. What color did you picture the marble?_____

   _____

3. What did you see for him pressing his cheek against it?_____

   _____

4. What did you see for the marble being "cool"?_____

3 **Third Sentence:** His fingers ran over the smooth surface.

What did those words make you picture?_____

_____

_____

1. What did you picture for Michelangelo's fingers?_____

_____

2. What did you picture for the smooth surface?_____

_____

3. What did you see for him touching the surface?_____

_____

4. What did you picture for his mood?_____

_____

4 **Fourth Sentence:** Finally, he began to imagine a figure he thought was inside.

What did those words make you picture?_____

_____

_____

1. What did you picture for Michelangelo looking at the marble?_____

_____

2. Did you see him staring at it for a long time or a short time?_____

_____

3. What did you picture for "a figure he thought was inside"?_____

_____

4. Were you picturing this up close or from far away?_____

_____

5 **Fifth Sentence:** The great sculptor picked up his chisel and began to sculpt the statue of David.

What did those words make you picture?_____

_____

_____

1. What did you picture for Michelangelo picking up his chisel?_____

_____

2. What did the chisel look like? Was it big or little, sharp or dull, or...?

_____

3. What did you see him doing with the chisel?_____

_____

Picture Summary:

Number your images in order.

☐ Michelangelo finally imagined the figure he thought was inside the stone.

☐ He picked up his chisel and began to sculpt the statue of David.

☐ Michelangelo often went to the quarry to look at the raw blocks of marble.

☐ He pressed his cheek against the stone and ran his fingers over it.

Critical Thinking

Write a Word Summary:

_____

_____

_____

_____

_____

Main Idea:

Check the box that best describes all your images—the main idea.

☐ Michelangelo found David trapped in a block of stone.

☐ Michelangelo looked at and touched a large block of stone and began to chisel the statue of David.

☐ Michelangelo often went to the quarry to look at the blocks of marble and touch the cool surface.

HOT Questions:

1. Why do you think Michelangelo often went to the quarry?_____

_____

2. Why do you think he pressed his cheek to the marble?_____

_____

3. What do you think it means that he began to imagine a figure inside the marble?_____

_____

4. Do you think there was really a person in the marble? Explain. _____

_____

5. Do you think it took him a long time to think of the figure inside the raw marble? Why or why not?_____

_____

6. Do you think the statue of David was big or little? Explain. _____

_____

Make up a story about going to a quarry, finding marble, and creating something.

_____

_____

_____

_____

_____

_____

_____

_____

_____

_____

_____

_____

_____

_____

_____

_____

_____

_____

Did you use all of the Structure Words? Check each one you used.

☐ What   ☐ Size   ☐ Color   ☐ Number   ☐ Shape   ☐ Where
☐ Movement   ☐ Mood   ☐ Background   ☐ Perspective   ☐ When   ☐ Sound

7 Swallows of Capistrano

Every year, on March 19, the little swallows of Capistrano fly home. On that day, large crowds stand in the middle of the church yard waiting for the sun to rise. As the first rays of sunlight appear, the people scan the clear blue sky. They cheer as a large flock of little birds comes into view. The church bells ring as lots of little swallows land in trees and under the eaves of the church.

Vocabulary:

swallow: a type of small songbird
Capistrano: the mission in the city of San Juan Capistrano, California
mission: an old church
scan: to quickly look for something
flock: a group of birds
eaves: the outer edge of a roof

---

1 First Sentence: Every year, on March 19, the little swallows of Capistrano fly home.

What did those words make you picture?_____

_____

_____

1. What did you picture for the swallows?_____

_____

2. What size did you picture the birds?_____

_____

3. What color did you picture the little birds?_____

_____

4. How did you picture March?_____

_____

---

2 Second Sentence: On that day, large crowds stand in the middle of the church yard waiting for the sun to rise.

What did those words make you picture?_____

_____

_____

1. What did you picture for the crowd?_____

_____

2. Where did you picture the crowd standing?_____

_____

3. What did you see for the yard?_____

_____

4. What did you see for the sun about to rise?_____

_____

3 Third Sentence: As the first rays of sunlight appear, the people scan the clear blue sky.

What did those words make you picture?_____

_____

_____

1. What did you picture for the first rays of sunlight?_____

_____

2. What did you see for the people scanning the sky?_____

_____

3. What color did you picture the sky?_____

_____

4. How did you see the sky as "clear"?_____

_____

4 Fourth Sentence: They cheer as a large flock of little birds comes into view.

What did those words make you picture?_____

_____

_____

1. What did you picture for the crowd cheering?_____

_____

2. What did you see for the flock of birds?_____

_____

3. How many birds did you picture?_____

_____

4. Were you picturing all this up close or from far away?_____

_____

5 Fifth Sentence: The church bells ring as lots of little swallows land in trees and under the eaves of the church.

What did those words make you picture?_____

_____

_____

1. What did you picture for the church bells?_____

_____

2. What did you picture for the sound of the bells ringing?_____

_____

3. What did you see for the birds landing in the trees?_____

Picture Summary:

Number your images in order.

    The crowd cheers as a large flock of little birds arrives.

    The church bells ring as the sparrows land in trees and under the eaves of the church.

    As the first rays of sun appear, people scan the skies.

    Every year, on March 19, the swallows of Capistrano fly home.

Critical Thinking

Write a Word Summary:

_____

_____

_____

_____

_____

Main Idea:

Check the box that best describes all your images—the main idea.

☐ The church bells ring as the swallows land in the trees.

☐ People wait at Capistrano in the early morning and scan the skies.

☐ Every year on March 19, crowds of people wait for the swallows to return to Capistrano.

HOT Questions:

1. Why do you think the crowd waited in the church yard?_____

_____

2. Why do you think the crowd went to the yard so early?_____

_____

3. Why do you think the crowd scanned the sky?_____

_____

4. Why do you think the church bells were rung when the swallows appeared?_____

_____

5. Why do you think the swallows come back every year?_____

_____

6. Why do you think the people are so happy when the birds come home every year?_____

_____

Make up a story about going to the church and seeing the swallows return.

_____

_____

_____

_____

_____

_____

_____

_____

_____

_____

_____

_____

_____

_____

Did you use all of the Structure Words? Check each one you used.

- ☐ What
- ☐ Movement
- ☐ Size
- ☐ Mood
- ☐ Color
- ☐ Background
- ☐ Number
- ☐ Perspective
- ☐ Shape
- ☐ When
- ☐ Where
- ☐ Sound

8 The Longest Night

It is November 18, the last day of sunlight for the year in Barrow, Alaska. The people of the town bring their lunches and watch the sun rise and set in 90 minutes. For the short time the sun is out, they eat lunch, laugh, and play. Then they say goodbye to the sun as it dips below the horizon. For the next two months it will be night and then they will celebrate again when the sun comes back.

Vocabulary:

Barrow: a small town in the northernmost part of Alaska
Alaska: the largest state in the United States; it is very far north
horizon: the line you see where the sky seems to meet the earth
celebrate: have a party

1

First Sentence: It is November 18, the last day of sunlight for the year in Barrow, Alaska.

What did those words make you picture?_____

_____

_____

1. What did you picture for a day of sunlight?_____

_____

2. What did you picture for Alaska?_____

_____

3. What did you picture for the weather?_____

_____

4. What letters and numbers did you picture for the month and day? Write them in the air and then write them on paper.

2

Second Sentence: The people of the town bring their lunches and watch the sun rise and set in 90 minutes.

What did those words make you picture?_____

_____

_____

1. What did you picture for the people?_____

_____

2. What did you picture for the town?_____

_____

3. What did you see for their lunch?_____

_____

4. What did you see for the sun rising and setting?_____

3 **Third Sentence:** For the short time the sun is out, they eat lunch, laugh, and play.

What did those words make you picture?_____

_____

1. What did you see for the sun being out a short time?_____

_____

2. What did you picture the people eating?_____

_____

3. What did you picture for the people laughing?_____

_____

4. How did you see the people playing?_____

_____

4 **Fourth Sentence:** Then they say goodbye to the sun as it dips below the horizon.

What did those words make you picture?_____

_____

_____

1. What did you see for them saying goodbye to the sun?_____

_____

2. What did you picture for the horizon?_____

_____

3. What did you picture the sun doing?_____

_____

4. What did you picture for the sky as the sun went down?_____

_____

5 **Fifth Sentence:** For the next two months it will be night and then they will celebrate again when the sun comes back.

What did those words make you picture?_____

_____

1. What did you picture to show two months passing?_____

_____

2. What did you see for the sky during the next two months?_____

_____

3. What did you picture for the sun coming up again?_____

_____

Picture Summary:

Number your images in order.

It is November 18, the last day of sunlight for the year in Barrow, Alaska.

For two months, it will be night in Barrow.

The people say goodbye to the sun as it sets.

The people of Barrow laugh, play, and eat lunch in the sunshine.

33

Write a Word Summary:

_____

_____

_____

_____

_____

Main Idea:

Check the box that best describes all your images—the main idea.

☐ The people of Barrow, Alaska have a celebration on the last day of sunlight in the winter.

☐ The people of Barrow, Alaska eat lunch, laugh, and play while the sun is out.

☐ For the next two months it will be night in Barrow, Alaska.

HOT Questions:

1. Why do you think they wanted to watch the sun rise and set on that specific day?_____

_____

2. Why do you think the people celebrated for only 90 minutes?_____

_____

3. Do you think the day was short or long on November 18th?_____

_____

4. Why do you think the crowd wanted to say goodbye to the sun?_____

_____

5. Why do you think they wanted to celebrate when the sun came up again?_____

_____

6. What do you think the people might do for the two months they are in the dark with no sun?_____

_____

Make up a story about living in Barrow, Alaska when it is completely dark.

_____

_____

_____

_____

_____

_____

_____

_____

_____

_____

_____

_____

_____

_____

_____

_____

_____

Did you use all of the Structure Words? Check each one you used.

☐ What   ☐ Size   ☐ Color   ☐ Number   ☐ Shape   ☐ Where
☐ Movement   ☐ Mood   ☐ Background   ☐ Perspective   ☐ When   ☐ Sound

9 Lucky the Artist

An elephant named Lucky is a famous abstract artist. She paints her pictures by picking up a paintbrush with the end of her trunk. She often uses red and blue paint, brushing it onto a large white canvas. Her paintings are called abstract because they are a swirl of colors and not a specific picture. Her paintings are sold and the money is used to save elephants in the wild.

Vocabulary:

abstract: a type of art that is colors and shapes but does not look like real people or things
trunk: the long nose of an elephant
canvas: a heavy piece of cloth that artists paint on

---

1 **First Sentence:** An elephant named Lucky is a famous abstract artist.

What did those words make you picture?_____
_____
_____

1. What did you picture for Lucky?_____
_____

2. What did you see for an elephant that is an artist?_____
_____

3. What did you picture for her being famous?_____
_____

4. Did you picture this from far away or up close?_____
_____

2 **Second Sentence:** She paints her pictures by picking up a paintbrush with the end of her trunk.

What did those words make you picture?_____
_____
_____

1. What did you picture for Lucky picking up the paintbrush?_____
_____

2. What did you picture for her trunk?_____
_____

3. What did you see for the paintbrush in her trunk?_____
_____

4. What did you see for her painting with her trunk?_____
_____

3 **Third Sentence:** She often uses red and blue paint, brushing it onto a large white canvas.

What did those words make you picture?_____

_____

1. What did you picture for the paint—in large buckets, small buckets, or...?

_____

2. What colors did you picture for the paint?_____

_____

3. Did you see Lucky moving the brush with small strokes or with big strokes?

_____

4. What did you picture for the canvas?_____

4 **Fourth Sentence:** Her paintings are called abstract because they are a swirl of colors and not a specific picture.

What did those words make you picture?_____

_____

_____

1. What did you picture for a "swirl" of colors on the canvas?_____

_____

2. What colors did you picture on the canvas?_____

_____

3. What size did you picture for the painting?_____

_____

4. Were you seeing this up close or from far away?_____

_____

5 **Fifth Sentence:** Her paintings are sold and the money is used to save elephants in the wild.

What did those words make you picture?_____

_____

_____

1. What did you picture for her paintings being sold?_____

_____

2. What did you see for elephants in the wild?_____

_____

3. What did you see for elephants being saved in the wild?_____

_____

Picture Summary:

Number your images in order.

▢   Lucky likes to use red and blue paint on a large white canvas.

▢   An elephant named Lucky is an artist.

▢   Lucky's abstract paintings are sold to raise money to help wild elephants.

▢   Lucky picks up the paintbrush with her trunk.

Write a Word Summary:

_____

_____

_____

_____

Main Idea:

Check the box that best describes all your images—the main idea.

☐ Lucky often brushes red and blue paint onto a white canvas.

☐ Lucky the elephant paints a swirl of colors and not a specific picture on a large canvas.

☐ Lucky the elephant is an artist whose paintings are sold to save elephants in the wild.

HOT Questions:

1. Do you think it is unusual for an elephant to be an artist? Why or why not?_____

_____

2. Why do you think Lucky uses her trunk to paint and not her feet?_____

_____

3. Why do you think Lucky paints on a large canvas?_____

_____

4. Why do you think she paints abstract art and not pictures of animals and trees?_____

_____

5. Why do you think many people want to buy her paintings?_____

_____

6. Why do you think the money is used to help wild elephants?_____

_____

Make up a story about an elephant being saved in the wild.

_____

_____

_____

_____

_____

_____

_____

_____

_____

_____

_____

_____

_____

_____

_____

_____

_____

Did you use all of the Structure Words? Check each one you used.

☐ What   ☐ Size   ☐ Color   ☐ Number   ☐ Shape   ☐ Where

☐ Movement   ☐ Mood   ☐ Background   ☐ Perspective   ☐ When   ☐ Sound

10 Lindbergh's Flight

Charles Lindbergh was the first to fly an airplane by himself across the Atlantic Ocean. On the morning of the flight, he watched as cans of gas were poured into the small plane's huge fuel tanks. He grabbed five sandwiches and a bottle of water, and then climbed into the airplane. He put on his goggles, placed wads of cotton in his ears, and started up his airplane. He flew alone for over 33 hours without stopping, landing in Paris to a crowd of cheering people.

Vocabulary:

fuel tank: a large tank that holds gas
goggles: glasses to keep a person's eyes safe
wad: a small round ball
Paris: a city in France, across the Atlantic Ocean from the

---

1 **First Sentence:** Charles Lindbergh was the first to fly an airplane by himself across the Atlantic Ocean.

What did those words make you picture?_____
_____
_____

1. What did you picture for Charles Lindbergh?_____

2. What did you picture for the Atlantic?_____

3. What did you see for Lindbergh flying across the Atlantic?_____

4. Did you see him flying alone or with another person?_____

---

2 **Second Sentence:** On the morning of the flight, he watched as cans of gas were poured into the small plane's huge fuel tanks.

What did those words make you picture?_____
_____

1. What did you picture for Lindbergh watching?_____

2. What did you picture for the gas being poured?_____

3. What did you picture for the size of the plane?_____

4. What did you see for the fuel tanks?_____

3 **Third Sentence:** He grabbed five sandwiches and a bottle of water, and then climbed in the airplane.

What did those words make you picture?_____

_____

1. What did you picture for Lindbergh "grabbing"?_____

_____

2. What did you see him grabbing?_____

_____

3. How many sandwiches did you picture him taking?_____

_____

4. What did you picture for Lindbergh getting into his small plane?_____

_____

4 **Fourth Sentence:** He put on his goggles, placed wads of cotton in his ears, and started up his airplane.

What did those words make you picture?_____

_____

_____

1. What did you picture for "goggles"?_____

_____

2. What did you see for Lindbergh putting on goggles?_____

_____

3. What did you see for him putting cotton in his ears?_____

_____

4. What did you picture for the sound of the plane starting up?_____

_____

5 **Fifth Sentence:** He flew alone for over 33 hours without stopping, landing in Paris to a crowd of cheering people.

What did those words make you picture?_____

_____

1. What did you picture for him flying alone—was he sleepy, hungry, thirsty, scared?

_____

2. What did you see for him flying without stopping?_____

_____

3. What did you picture for him landing in Paris?_____

_____

Picture Summary:

Number your images in order.

[ ] Lindbergh put on his goggles and started up his airplane.

[ ] Lindbergh flew alone for over 33 hours, then landed in Paris.

[ ] Lindbergh grabbed sandwiches and water and climbed into his plane.

[ ] Lindbergh watched as his plane's fuel tanks were filled on the morning of his flight.

Critical Thinking

Write a Word Summary:

_____

_____

_____

_____

Main Idea:

Check the box that best describes all your images—the main idea.

☐ Large cans of gas were poured into the plane's fuel tank before Lindbergh's flight.

☐ Charles Lindbergh prepared his plane before becoming the first person to fly across the Atlantic alone.

☐ Charles Lindberg put on his goggles and placed wads of cotton in his ears.

HOT Questions:

1. Why do you think Lindbergh wanted to cross the Atlantic Ocean alone?_____

_____

2. Why do you think the plane needed to have huge fuel tanks?_____

_____

3. Why do you think Lindbergh took five sandwiches and not just one?_____

_____

4. Why do you think Lindbergh put cotton in his ears?_____

_____

5. Do you think Lindbergh flew high or low in the air?_____

_____

6. Why do you think this is a famous flight in history?_____

_____

Make up a story about Lindbergh all by himself flying over the ocean for hours.

_____

_____

_____

_____

_____

_____

_____

_____

_____

_____

_____

_____

_____

_____

_____

_____

_____

_____

_____

Did you use all of the Structure Words? Check each one you used.

| ☐ What | ☐ Size | ☐ Color | ☐ Number | ☐ Shape | ☐ Where |
| ☐ Movement | ☐ Mood | ☐ Background | ☐ Perspective | ☐ When | ☐ Sound |

11 Bike and Climb

Goran Kropp wanted to climb the highest mountain in the world without any help. So he packed his bike with food and clothes and began to ride from Sweden to Nepal. For 7,000 miles, he pedaled over hills and mountains. After four months on the road, he reached the base of Mount Everest. The young man put on his climbing gear and began to climb the world's highest peak. After reaching the top, he took a few pictures and climbed back down. Then Kropp hopped on his bike and rode all the way home. The whole trip took him a year!

Vocabulary:

Goran Kropp: a Swedish climber
Sweden: a country in Northern Europe
Nepal: a country in Asia between China and India
Mt. Everest: the highest mountain in the world
gear: special clothes and equipment

1 **First and Second Sentences:** Goran Kropp wanted to climb the highest mountain in the world without any help. So he packed his bike with food and clothes and began to ride from Sweden to Nepal.

What did those words make you picture?_____

_____

_____

1. What did you picture for Goran Kropp?_____

_____

2. What did you picture for the highest mountain in the world?_____

_____

3. What did you see for how Kropp packed his bike?_____

_____

4. What did you picture for Kropp riding his bike from Sweden to Nepal?

2 **Third and Fourth Sentences:** For 7,000 miles, he pedaled over hills and mountains. After four months on the road, he reached the base of Mount Everest.

What did those words make you picture?_____

_____

_____

1. What did you picture to show the 7,000 miles he biked?_____

_____

2. What did you see for him pedaling over hills and mountains?_____

_____

3. What did you see Kropp doing when he reached Mount Everest?____

_____

4. How did you picture "four months" passing?_____

3 **Fifth and Sixth Sentences:** The young man put on his climbing gear and began to climb the world's highest peak. After reaching the top, he took a few pictures and climbed back down.

What did those words make you picture? _____

_____

1. What did you picture for Kropp climbing the mountain? _____

_____

2. What did you see for him at the top? _____

_____

3. What did you see for him taking pictures? _____

_____

4. What did you see for him climbing back down? _____

_____

4 **Seventh and Eighth Sentences:** Then Kropp hopped on his bike and rode all the way home. The whole trip took him a year!

What did those words make you picture? _____

_____

_____

1. What did you picture for Kropp now? _____

_____

2. How did you see him biking—slow or fast? _____

_____

3. What did you picture for where Kropp ended his trip? _____

_____

4. How did you picture this taking him a year? _____

_____

Picture Summary:

Number your images in order.

☐ Goran Kropp took some pictures and then climbed down.

☐ Goran Kropp rode his bike home.

☐ Goran Kropp climbed up Mt. Everest.

☐ Goran Kropp rode his bike from Sweden to Nepal.

Write a Word Summary:

_____

_____

_____

_____

_____

_____

_____

Critical Thinking

Main Idea:

Check the box that best describes all your images—the main idea.

☐ Goran Kropp spent a year riding his bike to Nepal, climbing Mt. Everest and then riding back home.

☐ Goran Kropp put on his climbing gear and began to climb the world's highest peak.

☐ Goran Kropp took a few pictures on the top of Mt. Everest and then climbed back down.

HOT Questions:

1. Why do you think Kropp rode his bike to Nepal and didn't take a train?_____

_____

2. Why do you think he needed to pack food and clothes?_____

_____

3. Why do you think it took four months for him to bike to Nepal?_____

_____

4. Why do you think he wanted to climb Mount Everest alone?_____

_____

5. Why do you think Kropp took pictures at the top of Mount Everest?_____

_____

6. Do you think Kropp tried to take some pictures at the top with himself in the picture? Why or why not?_____

_____

7. Why do you think this whole trip took him a year?_____

_____

Make up a story about riding a bike on a long, long trip.

_____

_____

_____

_____

_____

_____

_____

_____

_____

_____

_____

_____

_____

_____

_____

Did you use all of the Structure Words? Check each one you used.

☐ What   ☐ Size   ☐ Color   ☐ Number   ☐ Shape   ☐ Where

☐ Movement   ☐ Mood   ☐ Background   ☐ Perspective   ☐ When   ☐ Sound

12 The Lake People

High on a clear blue lake in Peru, the Uros people live on floating islands made of reeds. For hundreds of years, the people have used reeds to build the land for their homes. The bundles of reeds are placed in layers to form the islands. Then houses, also made of reeds, are built on top. Reeds are often added to the islands to make sure they stay a safe place to live. They even use reeds to build boats to move around the huge lake.

Vocabulary:

Peru: a country in South America
reeds: a type of tall thin grass that grows near water
floating: staying on top of water; not sinking
bundles: bunches; a group of things that are tied together

---

1 **First and Second Sentences:** High on a clear blue lake in Peru, the Uros people live on floating islands made of reeds. For hundreds of years, the people have used reeds to build the land for their homes.

What did those words make you picture?_____

_____

_____

1. What did you picture for the lake?_____

2. What did you picture for the floating islands?_____

3. What did you picture for the Uros people?_____

4. What did you see for the reeds?_____

---

2 **Third and Fourth Sentences:** The bundles of reeds are placed in layers to form the islands. Then houses, also made of reeds, are built on top.

What did those words make you picture?_____

_____

_____

1. What did you picture for the bundles of reeds?_____

2. What did you see for how they formed the islands?_____

3. Where did you picture them building the houses?_____

4. Did you picture them building large heavy homes, or were they small and light?

3 **Fifth and Sixth Sentences:** Reeds are often added to the islands to make sure they stay a safe place to live. They even use reeds to build boats to move around the huge lake.

What did those words make you picture?_____

_____

_____

1. What did you picture for them adding reeds to the island?_____

_____

2. Did you picture them adding reeds to the top or the bottom of the island?

_____

3. What did you picture for the boats? _____

_____

4. What did you see for the lake?_____

_____

Picture Summary:

Number your images in order.

☐ Reeds are added to the islands to make sure they stay afloat.

☐ The Uros people built floating islands out of reeds on a lake.

☐ Reeds are used to build their boats.

☐ Reeds are used to build their houses.

Write a Word Summary:

_____

_____

_____

_____

_____

_____

_____

Critical Thinking

Main Idea:

Check the box that best describes all your images—the main idea.

☐ The Uros people use reeds to build everything they need to live on floating islands.

☐ Reeds are often added to the islands to make sure they are a safe place to live.

☐ The Uros people live on floating islands in Peru.

HOT Questions:

1. Why do you think these people made floating islands?_____

_____

2. Why do you think they didn't build their homes on the ground?_____

_____

3. Why do you think they used reeds to build the houses instead of wood or bricks?_____

_____

4. Why do you think they need to keep adding more layers of reeds to the islands?_____

_____

5. Why do you think they needed to build the boats?_____

_____

6. Why do you think they used reeds to build the boats too?_____

_____

7. What problems do you think they might have living on a floating island?_____

_____

Make up a story about being a Uros and living on a floating island.

_____

_____

_____

_____

_____

_____

_____

_____

_____

_____

_____

_____

_____

_____

_____

_____

_____

Did you use all of the Structure Words? Check each one you used.

| ☐ What | ☐ Size | ☐ Color | ☐ Number | ☐ Shape | ☐ Where |
| ☐ Movement | ☐ Mood | ☐ Background | ☐ Perspective | ☐ When | ☐ Sound |

13 Flying Sharks

Near Seal Island, South Africa, the great white sharks are called "flying sharks." The huge sharks swim near the coast of the island in search of food. When a small black seal swims above, a giant shark gets ready. With a sudden burst of speed, he takes aim and propels his huge body through the water. He launches himself into the air with his deadly mouth, full of sharp teeth, opened wide. With a huge splash, the shark flops back into the ocean. Sometimes the shark misses his meal and then the lucky seal swims away.

Vocabulary:

great white: a type of shark that can be over 21 feet long
burst: moved with great power
propels: moves forward
launches: moves into the air

---

1 **First and Second Sentences:** Near Seal Island, South Africa, the great white sharks are called "flying sharks." The huge sharks swim near the coast of the island in search of food.

What did those words make you picture?_____

_____

1. What did you picture for the shark?_____

2. What did you see for a "flying shark"?_____

3. What did you picture for Seal Island?_____

4. What did you see for the shark swimming and searching?_____

---

2 **Third and Fourth Sentences:** When a small black seal swims above, a giant shark gets ready. With a sudden burst of speed, he takes aim and propels his huge body through the water.

What did those words make you picture?_____

_____

1. What did you see for the seal?_____

2. What did you picture the shark doing when he saw the seal?_____

3. What did you see for him taking aim?_____

4. How did you see him propelling through the water?_____

3 **Fifth and Sixth Sentences:** He launches himself into the air with his deadly mouth, full of sharp teeth, opened wide. With a huge splash, the shark flops back into the ocean.

What did those words make you picture?_____

_____

_____

1. What did you see for the shark in the air?_____

_____

2. What did you picture for his mouth and his teeth?_____

_____

3. What did you see for the shark flying in the air?_____

_____

4. What did you hear for the splash?_____

_____

4 **Seventh Sentence:** Sometimes the shark misses his meal and then the lucky seal swims away.

What did those words make you picture?_____

_____

_____

1. What did you picture for the shark "missing his meal"?_____

_____

2. What did you picture the seal doing?_____

_____

3. What did you picture for the shark's mood if he missed the seal?____

_____

4. What do you picture for the seal's mood?_____

_____

Picture Summary:

Number your images in order.

☐ The shark launches himself into the air with his mouth, full of teeth, wide open.

☐ The shark swims near Seal Island in search of food, like a seal above him.

☐ The shark falls back into the water, sometimes without a seal in his mouth.

☐ The shark propels his body out of the water and into the air.

Write a Word Summary:

_____

_____

_____

_____

_____

_____

_____

Critical Thinking

Main Idea:

Check the box that best describes all your images—the main idea.

☐ The great white shark swims near Seal Island searching for food.

☐ The great white shark of Seal Island sometimes misses his meal, so the seal swims away.

☐ The great white sharks of Seal Island launch themselves into the air as they try to catch seals.

HOT Questions:

1. Why do you think the island was called "Seal Island"?_____

_____

2. Why do you think the shark was swimming near Seal Island?_____

_____

3. Why do you think these sharks are called "flying sharks"?_____

_____

4. Why do you think the shark swam very quickly at the seal?_____

_____

5. Why do you think the shark came out of the water and into the air?_____

_____

6. What do you think the seal did next if the shark missed?_____

_____

7. Why do you think the story said the seal was "lucky"?_____

_____

Make up a story about seeing a great white shark when you were swimming one day in the ocean.

_____

_____

_____

_____

_____

_____

_____

_____

_____

_____

_____

_____

_____

_____

_____

_____

Did you use all of the Structure Words? Check each one you used.

| ☐ What | ☐ Size | ☐ Color | ☐ Number | ☐ Shape | ☐ Where |
| ☐ Movement | ☐ Mood | ☐ Background | ☐ Perspective | ☐ When | ☐ Sound |

14 Tidal Wave!

Deep beneath the sea, the earth began to shake and a tidal wave was born. Huge ripples of water pushed across the sea. Faster and faster, the water moved until it reached a remote island. As the rushing sea came close to shore, a huge wave formed. The wave grew to 100 feet high, and then it crashed down on the beach and trees. In a moment, the giant wave washed everything living away and only an island of dirt was left.

Vocabulary:

tidal wave: a huge wave
ripples: waves of water
remote: far away
rushing: moving very quickly

---

1 **First and Second Sentences:** Deep beneath the sea, the earth began to shake and a tidal wave was born. Huge ripples of water pushed across the sea.

What did those words make you picture?_____

_____

_____

1. What did you picture for the earth under the sea?_____

2. What did you picture for the earth shaking?_____

3. What did you see for the water after the earth shook?_____

4. What did you picture for the tidal wave being born?_____

---

2 **Third and Fourth Sentences:** Faster and faster, the water moved until it reached a remote island. As the rushing sea came close to shore, a huge wave formed.

What did those words make you picture?_____

_____

_____

1. What did you picture for the water as it moved?_____

2. What did you picture for the remote island?_____

3. What did you see for the rushing sea?_____

4. What did you see for the wave forming?_____

3 **Fifth and Sixth Sentences:** The wave grew to 100 feet high, and then it crashed down on the beach and trees. In a moment, the giant wave washed everything living away and only an island of dirt was left.

What did those words make you picture?_____

_____

_____

1. What did you picture for the big wave?_____

_____

2. Did you see the wave being taller or smaller than the trees?_____

_____

3. What did you picture as the wave hit the beach?_____

_____

4. What did you see for the island after the wave washed everything away?

_____

Picture Summary:

Number your images in order.

⬛ The water moved faster and faster until it reached an island.

⬛ Deep beneath the sea, the earth began to shake and make the water move.

⬛ A giant wave washed everything away and only an island of dirt remained.

⬛ A huge wave, 100 feet high, formed and crashed down on the beach.

Write a Word Summary:

_____

_____

_____

_____

_____

_____

_____

_____

Main Idea:

Check the box that best describes all your images—the main idea.

☐ The earth began to shake, and sent ripples of water across the sea in all directions.

☐ The tidal wave grew 100 feet high and crashed down on the beach, leaving only dirt behind.

☐ An earthquake caused a tidal wave that washed away all the living things on an island.

HOT Questions:

1. What do you think happened under the sea that might have caused the earth to shake?_____

_____

2. Why do you think the wave continued to move across the sea and did not stop?_____

_____

3. How do you think the huge ripples may have affected the wave?_____

_____

4. Do you think a smaller tidal wave would have washed everything off the island? Why or why not?_____

_____

5. Why do you think everything living was washed off the island?_____

_____

6. Do you think it was good that this happened on a remote island? Explain._____

_____

7. What do you think would happen if a tidal wave this big rushed on shore in a city?_____

_____

Make up a story about anything you want!

_____

_____

_____

_____

_____

_____

_____

_____

_____

_____

_____

_____

_____

_____

_____

Did you use all of the Structure Words? Check each one you used.

☐ What   ☐ Size   ☐ Color   ☐ Number   ☐ Shape   ☐ Where
☐ Movement   ☐ Mood   ☐ Background   ☐ Perspective   ☐ When   ☐ Sound

15 The Cocoa King

Montezuma, a great Aztec king, loved to drink hot cocoa made without sugar. Servants gave him more than 50 gold cups filled with the bitter drink each day. All day the king sat on his throne and asked for more cocoa. Then he drank the cocoa and tossed the empty cups into a lake. He believed that cocoa made him wise and young. The recipe for the king's cocoa was thought to be so important that it was guarded and only given to rich people.

Vocabulary:

cocoa: a powder from cacao tree that is used to make chocolate
Montezuma: the ruler of the Aztec empire from 1502 to 1520
Aztec: an American Indian civilization that lived in Central Mexico
bitter: not sweet; with a strong taste

---

1 **First and Second Sentences:** Montezuma, a great Aztec king, loved to drink hot cocoa made without sugar. Servants gave him more than 50 gold cups filled with the bitter drink each day.

What did those words make you picture?_____

_____

_____

1. What did you picture for Montezuma?_____

_____

2. What did you picture for the cocoa?_____

_____

3. What did you picture for how it tasted without sugar?_____

_____

4. What did you see for the 50 gold cups? _____

_____

---

2 **Third and Fourth Sentences:** All day the king sat on his throne and asked for more cocoa. Then he drank the cocoa and tossed the empty cups into a lake.

What did those words make you picture?_____

_____

_____

1. What did you picture for his throne?_____

_____

2. What did you see for the king sitting on his throne?_____

_____

3. What did you see for him asking for more cocoa all day?_____

_____

4. What did you see for him tossing the cups into the lake?_____

_____

3 **Fifth and Sixth Sentences:** He believed that cocoa made him wise and young. The recipe for the king's cocoa was thought to be so important that it was guarded and only given to rich people.

What did those words make you picture? _____

_____

1. What did you picture for him believing cocoa made him young? _____

_____

2. What did you see for him believing it made him wise? _____

_____

3. What did you see for what they did with the recipe? _____

_____

4. What did you see for the rich people getting the recipe? _____

_____

Picture Summary:

Number your images in order.

Montezuma loved to drink cocoa made without sugar.

He tossed the empty cups into the lake.

He kept the recipe guarded and only gave it to the rich people.

His servants brought him more than 50 gold cups of cocoa each day.

Write a Word Summary:

_____

_____

_____

_____

_____

_____

_____

Main Idea:

Check the box that best describes all your images—the main idea.

☐ Montezuma tossed the empty gold cups into a lake.

☐ A hot bitter cocoa drink was loved by Montezuma and the rich Aztec people.

☐ Servants brought Montezuma more than 50 cups of cocoa each day.

HOT Questions:

1. Why do you think the king drank cocoa without sugar?_____

_____

2. Do you think if he had sugar he would have used it in his cocoa? Explain._____

_____

3. Why do you think the servants placed the cocoa in gold cups?_____

_____

4. Why do you think the king drank more than 50 cups a day?_____

_____

5. Do you think sugarless cocoa makes a person young? Explain._____

_____

6. Why do you think servants might be swimming in the lake after dark?_____

_____

7. Why do you think only rich people got the recipe and not poor people?_____

_____

Make up a story about cocoa making everyone young!

_____

_____

_____

_____

_____

_____

_____

_____

_____

_____

_____

_____

_____

_____

_____

Did you use all of the Structure Words? Check each one you used.

☐ What   ☐ Size   ☐ Color   ☐ Number   ☐ Shape   ☐ Where
☐ Movement   ☐ Mood   ☐ Background   ☐ Perspective   ☐ When   ☐ Sound

16 Mozart & the Empress

When Mozart was six years old, he was asked to play the harpsichord at the Austrian royal court. The pretty Empress smiled as the child genius sat down at the keyboard. With his feet dangling from the bench, he reached up to touch the white and black keys. The room was quiet as his tiny fingers flew back and forth across the keys. His beautiful music filled the room and dazzled the small crowd. Then, when he was finished, little Mozart jumped down from the bench and gave a big bow.

Vocabulary:

Mozart: a famous musician and composer
Empress: a queen
harpsichord: a keyboard instrument that came before the piano
Austrian: from Austria, in Europe
court: where a king and queen live
dangling: swinging above the floor
dazzled: amazed; wowed

---

1 **First and Second Sentences:** When Mozart was six years old, he was asked to play the harpsichord at the Austrian royal court. The pretty Empress smiled as the child genius sat down at the keyboard.

What did those words make you picture?_____

_____

_____

1. What did you picture for Mozart?_____

_____

2. What did you picture for the royal court?_____

_____

3. What did you picture for the Empress?_____

_____

4. What did you picture for the keyboard?_____

---

2 **Third and Fourth Sentences:** With his feet dangling from the bench, he reached up to touch the white and black keys. The room was quiet as his tiny fingers flew back and forth across the keys.

What did those words make you picture?_____

_____

_____

1. What did you see for the little Mozart on the bench?_____

_____

2. What did you picture him doing with his hands? _____

_____

3. What did you see for the room where he played the harpsichord?_____

_____

4. What sounds did you picture in the room as he began to play?_____

_____

3

Fifth and Sixth Sentences: His beautiful music filled the room and dazzled the small crowd. Then, when he was finished, little Mozart jumped down from the bench and gave a big bow.

What did those words make you picture?_____

_____

1. What did you picture for Mozart playing beautiful music?_____

_____

2. What did you see for a crowd of people listening to him?_____

_____

3. What did you see happening when little Mozart finished the song?

_____

4. What did you picture for him taking a bow?_____

_____

Picture Summary:

Number your images in order.

☐ Mozart played the harpsichord for the Austrian Empress when he was a child.

☐ Mozart jumped down from the bench and gave a big bow.

☐ The room was quiet as his beautiful music dazzled the small crowd.

☐ The Empress smiled as the six-year-old boy sat down at the harpsichord with his feet dangling.

Write a Word Summary:

_____

_____

_____

_____

_____

_____

Critical Thinking

Main Idea:

Check the box that best describes all your images—the main idea.

☐ Mozart gave a big bow after he finished playing for the Empress.

☐ When Mozart was a child, he performed in front of the Austrian royal court and dazzled them with his talent.

☐ Mozart's tiny fingers flew back and forth across the keys and the Empress loved his music.

HOTS Questions:

1. Why do you think the Empress smiled when little Mozart sat down at the keyboard?_____

_____

2. Why do you think Mozart was asked to play for the Empress?_____

_____

3. Why do you think his feet dangled from the bench?_____

_____

4. Why do you think the small crowd was quiet when Mozart started to play?_____

_____

5. Why do you think the crowd was dazzled?_____

_____

6. Why do you think the young Mozart was called a genius?_____

_____

7. What do you think happened to Mozart's musical talent as he grew up?_____

_____

Make up a story about an instrument you play or want to play.

_____

_____

_____

_____

_____

_____

_____

_____

_____

_____

_____

_____

_____

_____

_____

_____

Did you use all of the Structure Words? Check each one you used.

☐ What   ☐ Size   ☐ Color   ☐ Number   ☐ Shape   ☐ Where
☐ Movement   ☐ Mood   ☐ Background   ☐ Perspective   ☐ When   ☐ Sound

17 The Oregon Trail

The hot sun beats down on the white covered wagons as they start on the Oregon Trail. Three hundred wagons, each pulled by two oxen, roll slowly over the tall prairie grass. Tired of sitting in the bumpy wagons, giggling kids run up and down the line of covered wagons. Parents walk beside the oxen for mile after mile. Each night the whole wagon train stops and rests, but day after day they walk. Finally, six months later, they reach Oregon and their long journey to find a new home is over.

Vocabulary:

Oregon Trail: a path people once traveled to go to the West
covered wagon: a large wagon with a high cloth top
oxen: a type of large cattle
prairie: a large grassy flat area

---

1 **First and Second Sentences:** The hot sun beats down on the white covered wagons as they start on the Oregon Trail. Three hundred wagons, each pulled by two oxen, roll slowly over the tall prairie grass.

What did those words make you picture?_____

_____

_____

1. What did you picture for the covered wagons?_____

_____

2. What did you picture for the Oregon Trail?_____

_____

3. What did you picture for the oxen?_____

_____

4. Did you see the wagons moving slowly or quickly?_____

_____

---

2 **Third and Fourth Sentences:** Tired of sitting in the bumpy wagons, giggling kids run up and down the line of covered wagons. Parents walk beside the oxen for mile after mile.

What did those words make you picture?_____

_____

_____

1. What did you picture for the kids?_____

_____

2. What did you see for the wagons moving along?_____

_____

3. What sounds did you hear?_____

_____

4. What did you see for the parents?_____

_____

3 **Fifth and Sixth Sentences:** Each night the whole wagon train stops and rests, but day after day they walk. Finally, six months later, they reach Oregon and their long journey to find a new home is over.

What did those words make you picture?_____

_____

1. What did you picture for the wagon train at night?_____

_____

2. What did you picture for the people resting?_____

_____

3. What did you see the people doing when they woke up in the morning?

_____

4. What did you see them doing when they got to Oregon?_____

_____

Picture Summary:

Number these in order.

☐ The hot sun beats down on the wagons as they start on the Oregon Trail.

☐ Six months later, they reach Oregon and their long journey is over.

☐ The kids run up and down the line of covered wagons.

☐ Parents walk beside the wagons for miles and rest at night.

Write a Word Summary:

_____

_____

_____

_____

_____

_____

_____

Critical Thinking

Main Idea:

Check the box that best describes all your images—the main idea.

☐ Giggling kids run up and down the line of covered wagons on the Oregon Trail.

☐ For six months, a long line of covered wagons slowly moves along the Oregon Trail.

☐ Each night the whole wagon train stops and rests as they travel along the Oregon Trail.

HOT Questions:

1. Why do you think the people used covered wagons rather than open wagons?_____

_____

2. Why do you think the kids liked to run up and down the line of wagons?_____

_____

3. Why do you think a lot of people traveled together?_____

_____

4. Why do you think they didn't all ride in the back of the wagons?_____

_____

5. Why do you think the wagon train moved slowly?_____

_____

6. Why do you think the wagon train stopped at night?_____

_____

7. Do you think the covered wagons were white when they finished the trip? Explain._____

_____

Make up a story about being a child on the Oregon Trail.

Did you use all of the Structure Words? Check each one you used.
- [ ] What
- [ ] Movement
- [ ] Size
- [ ] Mood
- [ ] Color
- [ ] Background
- [ ] Number
- [ ] Perspective
- [ ] Shape
- [ ] When
- [ ] Where
- [ ] Sound

73

18 Henson's Muppets

Jim Henson created his famous Muppets when he was still in high school. A local television station wanted a puppeteer for their television show for kids. Jim got the job and made a puppet with a soft face that could move to show its feelings. Even though the TV show didn't last long, Jim and his "Muppets" were a big hit. He was asked to make some more Muppets for a new show that became very popular. Soon, kids from all over would know and love Kermit, Big Bird, and the rest of the Muppets.

Vocabulary:

Muppet: a special kind of puppet with wires to move the arms
created: made something new
puppeteer: a person who makes puppets move and talk

---

1 **First and Second Sentences:** Jim Henson created his famous Muppets when he was still in high school. A local television station wanted a puppeteer for their television show for kids.

What did those words make you picture?_____

_____

_____

1. What did you picture for Jim?_____

_____

2. What did you picture for a Muppet? _____

3. What did you picture for a puppeteer?_____

4. What did you see for a kids' television show?_____

---

2 **Third and Fourth Sentences:** Jim got the job and made a puppet with a soft face that could move to show its feelings. Even though the TV show didn't last long, Jim and his "Muppets" were a big hit.

What did those words make you picture?_____

_____

_____

1. What did you picture for Jim making a puppet?_____

2. What did you picture for the puppet's face?_____

3. What did you picture for how the face could move?_____

4. What did you see for Jim's "Muppets" being a big hit?_____

3 **Fifth and Sixth Sentences:** He was asked to make some more Muppets for a new show that became very popular. Soon, kids from all over would know and love Kermit, Big Bird, and the rest of the Muppets.

What did those words make you picture?_____

_____

1. What did you picture for Jim making some new Muppets?_____

_____

2. What did you picture for the new show?_____

_____

3. What did you picture for Kermit? _____

_____

4. What did you see for kids loving the Muppets?_____

_____

Picture Summary:

Number your images in order.

Jim Henson created the Muppets while he was in high school, when a local television station wanted a puppeteer for their kids' show.

Soon, kids from all over the world would know and love Kermit and the rest of the Muppets.

Jim made a puppet with a soft face that could move to show its feelings.

Jim's Muppets were a big hit and Jim was asked to put them on a new show that became very popular.

Write a Word Summary:

_____

_____

_____

_____

_____

_____

_____

_____

Critical Thinking

Main Idea:

Check the box that best describes all your images—the main idea.

☐ Jim Henson created puppets called Muppets, which became famous all over the world.

☐ Kids all over the world know Kermit, Big Bird and the rest of the Muppets.

☐ Jim Henson made his Muppets for a local television show for kids.

HOT Questions:

1. Why do you think a kids' television show might need a puppeteer?_____

_____

2. Why do you think Jim decided to make his puppet with a soft face?_____

_____

3. Why do you think it is important for a puppet to show feelings?_____

_____

4. Why do you think Jim's puppets were called Muppets?_____

_____

5. Why do you think Jim's Muppets were so popular?_____

_____

6. How do you think Jim felt when his Muppets became popular?_____

_____

7. Why do you think Jim may have kept creating more Muppets?_____

_____

Make up a story about Big Bird and Kermit the Frog going to the zoo.

_____

_____

_____

_____

_____

_____

_____

_____

_____

_____

_____

_____

_____

_____

_____

_____

Did you use all of the Structure Words? Check each one you used.

| ☐ What | ☐ Size | ☐ Color | ☐ Number | ☐ Shape | ☐ Where |
| ☐ Movement | ☐ Mood | ☐ Background | ☐ Perspective | ☐ When | ☐ Sound |

19 Hurricane Hunters

The hurricane hunters strapped themselves in their seats as they began their flight into the storm. They were silent as the pilot flew them straight into the strong winds and swirling rains. The weather pounded the plane while the crew checked the temperature and wind speed of the storm. They flew into the clear skies in the eye of the storm, where the ride was calm. For ten hours, the crew flew in and out of the storm to gather data that would help people survive future storms. With their fuel nearly gone, the brave hurricane hunters flew home.

Vocabulary:

hurricane: a very large storm with strong winds and rain
pounded: beat; hit
eye of the storm: the calm center of a hurricane
data: information

---

1 **First and Second Sentences:** The hurricane hunters strapped themselves in their seats as they began their flight into the storm. They were silent as the pilot flew them straight into the strong winds and swirling rains.

What did those words make you picture?_____

_____

_____

1. What did you picture for the hurricane hunters?_____

_____

2. What did you picture for them in their seats?_____

_____

3. What did you see for the hurricane?_____

_____

4. What did you see for the plane flying into the hurricane?_____

---

2 **Third and Fourth Sentences:** The weather pounded the plane while the crew checked the temperature and wind speed of the storm. They flew into the clear skies in the eye of the storm, where the ride was calm.

What did those words make you picture?_____

_____

_____

1. What did you picture for the plane being pounded by the weather?_____

_____

2. What did you see the crew doing now?_____

_____

3. What did you picture for the wind speed?_____

_____

4. What did you see for the eye of the storm?_____

_____

3

Fifth and Sixth Sentences: For ten hours, the crew flew in and out of the storm to gather data that would help people survive future storms. With their fuel nearly gone, the brave hurricane hunters flew home.

What did those words make you picture?_____

_____

_____

1. What did you see for the plane flying in and out of the storm?_____

   _____

2. What did you picture to show that ten hours had passed? Did you picture a clock or words and numbers?

   _____

3. What did you see to show their fuel being nearly gone?_____

   _____

4. What did you see for the hurricane hunters flying home? _____

   _____

Picture Summary:

Number your images in order.

◻ With their fuel nearly gone, the brave hurricane hunters flew home.

◻ The hurricane hunters strapped themselves into their seats and flew into the strong winds and swirling rains of the storm.

◻ They checked temperature and wind speed in the pounding weather.

◻ Then they flew into the clear skies in the eye of the storm, where the ride was calm.

Write a Word Summary:

_____

_____

_____

_____

_____

_____

_____

Critical Thinking

Main Idea:

Check the box that best describes all your images—the main idea.

☐ Hurricane hunters fly back and forth through hurricanes to gather information about the storms.

☐ Hurricane hunters are silent as the pilot flies them into the strong winds and rains of the storms.

☐ The weather pounded the plane while the crew checked the temperature and wind speed.

HOT Questions:

1. Why do you think the hurricane hunters had to strap themselves into their seats?_____

_____

2. Why do you think they became silent when the pilot flew the plane into the hurricane?_____

_____

3. Why do you think it was important to fly into the hurricane?_____

_____

4. Why do you think they measured the wind speed and temperature?_____

_____

5. Why do you think they flew in and out of the storm many times?_____

_____

6. Why do you think they risked their lives to gather data?_____

_____

7. Why do you think they are called hurricane hunters?_____

_____

Make up a story about Jim, a hurricane hunter, in the biggest hurricane of the year.

_____

_____

_____

_____

_____

_____

_____

_____

_____

_____

_____

_____

_____

_____

_____

_____

_____

_____

Did you use all of the Structure Words? Check each one you used.

☐ What   ☐ Size   ☐ Color   ☐ Number   ☐ Shape   ☐ Where
☐ Movement   ☐ Mood   ☐ Background   ☐ Perspective   ☐ When   ☐ Sound

20 Sacagawea

Sacagawea, a young American Indian woman, became the guide for the Lewis and Clark Expedition in America. She saved the team many times with her brains and bravery. Once she was in a boat with her baby boy as the group of men sailed up a river. A storm blew in and a huge gust of wind tipped her boat onto its side. The men only watched as books and tools fell into the water, but she moved quickly. Holding her baby in one arm, she pulled the supplies from the river with the other. Then they could continue their journey west to the Pacific Ocean.

Vocabulary:

expedition: a trip made by a group to explore new lands
gust: a sudden large wind
Lewis and Clark: two men sent to explore the West from 1804 to 1806
Sacagawea: a famous American Indian woman

---

1 **First and Second Sentences:** Sacagawea, a young American Indian woman, became the guide for the Lewis and Clark Expedition in America. She saved the team many times with her brains and bravery.

What did those words make you picture? _____
_____
_____

1. What did you picture for Sacagawea?_____
_____

2. What did you picture for her as a guide?_____
_____

3. What did you see for the expedition?_____
_____

4. How did you see her saving the expedition?_____

---

2 **Third and Fourth Sentences:** Once she was in a boat with her baby boy as the group of men sailed up a river. A storm blew in and a huge gust of wind tipped her boat onto its side.

What did those words make you picture?_____
_____
_____

1. What did you see for Sacagawea in the boat?_____
_____

2. Where did you picture her baby?_____
_____

3. What did you see for them sailing on a river?_____
_____

4. What did you picture for the boat tipping over?_____

3 **Fifth and Sixth Sentences:** The men only watched as books and tools fell into the water, but she moved quickly. Holding her baby in one arm, she pulled the supplies from the river with the other.

What did those words make you picture?_____

_____

_____

1. What did you picture for tools?_____

_____

2. What did you see the men doing?_____

_____

3. What did you see Sacagawea doing?_____

_____

4. How did you see her holding her baby?_____

4 **Seventh Sentence:** Then they could continue their journey west to the Pacific Ocean.

What did those words make you picture?_____

_____

_____

1. What did you picture for where they were heading?_____

_____

2. What did you picture for the west?_____

_____

3. What did you picture for the Pacific Ocean?_____

_____

4. What did you see for their mood when they reached the Pacific Ocean?

_____

Picture Summary:

Number your images in order.

▢ Sacagawea moved quickly to grab the supplies while she held her son.

▢ Sacagawea became the guide for the Lewis and Clark Expedition.

▢ A sudden gust of wind tipped over the boat, and the tools and books fell into the water.

▢ Sacagawea was in a boat with the men and their supplies.

Write a Word Summary:

_____

_____

_____

_____

_____

_____

Main Idea:

Check the box that best describes all your images—the main idea.

☐ Sacagawea was brave and smart and saved the Lewis and Clark Expedition many times.

☐ Sacagawea carried her baby son as they sailed up a river on the Lewis and Clark Expedition.

☐ Sacagawea's quick action saved the equipment that fell into the water so the Lewis and Clark Expedition could continue.

HOT Questions:

1. Why do you think the expedition was on the river rather than on land?_____

_____

2. Why do you think Sacagawea was with the expedition?_____

_____

3. Why do you think she had her baby with her?_____

_____

4. Why do you think the boat may have tipped over?_____

_____

5. Why do you think Sacagawea acted more quickly than the men?_____

_____

6. Why do you think Sacagawea's actions helped save the expedition?_____

_____

7. How else do you think Sacagawea may have helped the expedition succeed?_____

_____

Make up a story about Sacagawea saving the Lewis and Clark Expedition.

Did you use all of the Structure Words? Check each one you used.

☐ What   ☐ Size   ☐ Color   ☐ Number   ☐ Shape   ☐ Where
☐ Movement   ☐ Mood   ☐ Background   ☐ Perspective   ☐ When   ☐ Sound

Notes:

Analysis of Student Performance:

Notes:

Analysis of Student Performance:

Notes:

Analysis of Student Performance:

_____

_____

_____

_____

_____

_____

_____

_____

_____

_____

_____

_____

_____

_____

_____

_____

Visualizing and Verbalizing® Graded Workbooks Color Coding

The colored checkers along the book's spine represent the grade level of the workbook. For example, the four red checkers indicate that the workbook is written at a fourth grade reading level. The colored star helps differentiate between books a, b, and c in each workbook set.